HÄGAR the horrible

on holiday

℞
RAVETTE BOOKS

This edition first published by Ravette Books Limited 1990

Printed and Bound
for Ravette Books Limited,
3 Glenside Estate, Star Road, Partridge Green,
Horsham, West Sussex RH13 8RA
by Cox & Wyman Ltd, Reading

ISBN: 1 85304 305 2

HAMLET LUCKY EDDIE HÄGAR HELGA SNERT HONI

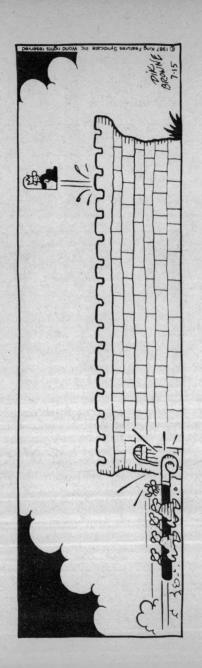

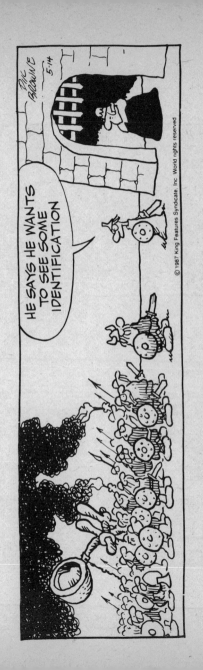

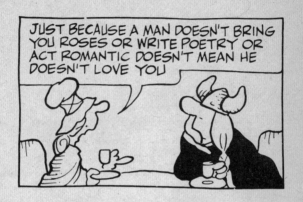

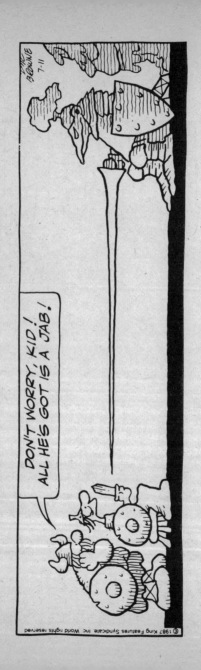

THE FACTS OF LIFE # 1

A FEW THINGS FOR YOU TO REMEMBER...

NEVER WEAR YELLOW. BLONDES WHO WEAR YELLOW LOOK LIKE BANANAS!

AND NEVER, NEVER, NEVER TRUST A MAN WHO SAYS, "TRUST ME!"

HELGA SAYS I NEVER PAY ATTENTION TO HOW SHE LOOKS ANYMORE

I'LL SURPRISE HER!

HI, HELGA... SAY! YOU'VE PUT ON A LITTLE WEIGHT, HAVEN'T YOU?